Meeting Mozart

Explorer Challenge

Find out who wrote this
piece of music ...

OXFORD
UNIVERSITY PRESS

Nadim was learning to play the piano. He enjoyed his lessons and now he could play with both hands. In fact, he was quite good, so his dad got him a keyboard.

Nadim took the keyboard to show Biff and Chip.

"It plays different sounds, like an organ or guitar," he said. "It can play a drum beat, and you can record what you are playing."

Nadim had learned to play 'Walking in the Air'.
He played that and then a minuet by Bach.

"I like this one the best," he said. "A minuet is a
sort of grand dance."

Mum came into the kitchen to listen. "You play really well, Nadim," she said.

Just then, her phone rang. "It's an important call," she said. "Why don't you take the keyboard up to Biff's bedroom?"

"Play something else, Nadim," said Chip. "Try it with the drum beat on."

Then the key began to glow. Nadim was still holding the keyboard when they were whisked into a new adventure.

The key took them back in time. They were in a
beautiful room with lots of mirrors.

"What an enormous room!" said Biff. "We must be in
some sort of palace."

Through a doorway they could see a boy sitting at an instrument that looked like a small piano.

"I think that's a harpsichord," said Nadim.

Then a man strode in. "Why have you stopped playing, Wolfgang?" he demanded.

"I'm tired, Father," the boy said. "I don't want to play this evening."

"You must!" The man sighed and held up his hands. "The Archduke expects you to play. We cannot afford to upset him. He pays us to hear you play."

"You must practise for the concert tonight," the man went on. "No more nonsense! Now play!"

The boy began to cry. "I won't!" he sobbed. "I can't." He jumped up and ran out of the room.

The man saw the children.

"We've been spotted, too," said Biff. "We'd better run. Come on! Follow the boy."

"Thieves! I'll have you locked up," shouted the man. "Guards! Come quickly!"

The boy ran up steps, round corners, through doors and along corridors. The children ran after him, trying to keep up.

"This is an enormous place," panted Chip. "I wonder where we are."

At last the boy ran into a room, slammed the door and locked it.

"Well, we got away from that man," said Biff. "But now what do we do? Shall we try knocking?"

Chip listened at the door. "I can hear him crying."
He tapped on the door gently. "Er … hello …
Wolfgang," he called softly.

A shoe thudded against the door. "Go away!"
came a voice from inside.

"Wolfgang!" gasped Biff. "I've had a thought! Do you think he might be Mozart? He was called Wolfgang."

"Mozart, eh?" said Nadim thoughtfully. "I think I know how to get him to open the door."

Nadim switched on the keyboard and played a note.
"Great!" he said. "It still plays even though we
have gone back in time. You two hold it and I will play
'Walking in the Air'."

Nadim had only played a few bars when the door suddenly opened.

The boy's eyes were wide with astonishment. "That's an amazing instrument. It sounds tuneful, but so strange!" he said. "What a simple tune! What else can you play?"

They went inside and Wolfgang locked the door.
Nadim played the minuet by Bach.

"That's better," said Wolfgang. "Now keep playing
with your left hand. I'll add a few … twiddly bits …
to the tune."

"It's amazing," laughed Wolfgang. "I don't have to strike the keys as hard as I do on the harpsichord. This instrument is brilliant."

"You play it brilliantly, too," said Nadim.

At that moment, there was loud knocking on the door.

It was Wolfgang's father. "Open the door," he called. "Now, please, Wolfgang! The Archduke wishes to hear you play. If you don't, we will be ruined. Do you want me to break this door down and drag you on to the stage?"

Wolfgang began to cry. "I can't play tonight," he sobbed. "The Archduke is so scary and bad-tempered. I get terrible stage fright and I am too nervous to play."

At that moment, Nadim had a brilliant idea.

"Your Imperial Highness," announced Wolfgang's father. "I present my son, Wolfgang Mozart, who will start by performing with another young musician, Nadim."

"Nadim's wearing a white wig," hissed Biff, trying not to giggle.

Nadim laid the keyboard on a table and Wolfgang whispered, "Start by playing with both hands. When I say 'now', just play with your left hand."

As Nadim began to play, something terrible happened. The keyboard went dead. The battery had run out.

The audience began to fidget. The Archduke frowned and sniffed impatiently.

"Don't panic, Wolfgang," whispered Nadim. "We'll play the harpsichord instead."

"Well, hit the keys harder than you do on your instrument," said Wolfgang. "Let's do it!"

First, they played the minuet by Bach with
Wolfgang adding lots of notes. Then, to Nadim's
surprise, Wolfgang began to play 'Walking in the Air'.

"Keep playing the left hand – but slowly,"
whispered Wolfgang.

"Well," said the Archduke to Wolfgang. "If you play tunes like that, you will never be much of a musician." He looked at Nadim. "You need to practise, young man," he said. "And you need to dress properly."

"My heart sank when the keyboard went dead,"
said Biff. "But you were great on the harpsichord."

"Thanks, Nadim," said Wolfgang. "You helped me
get over my stage fright. But don't rely on that funny
instrument. Get a proper harpsichord."

Just then, the key glowed.

"I've finished my phone call," called Mum. "Let me hear Nadim play a couple more tunes."

They took the keyboard downstairs and Nadim plugged it in. He pressed the play button and an amazing thing happened.

The keyboard had recorded Nadim playing 'Walking in
the Air' with Wolfgang.

"That's rather good," said Mum. "Who's that playing?"

"Wow! It's me actually playing with Mozart," said Nadim.

"Hmm, yes!" laughed Mum. "I believe you!"

Retell the Story

Look at the pictures and retell the story in your own words.

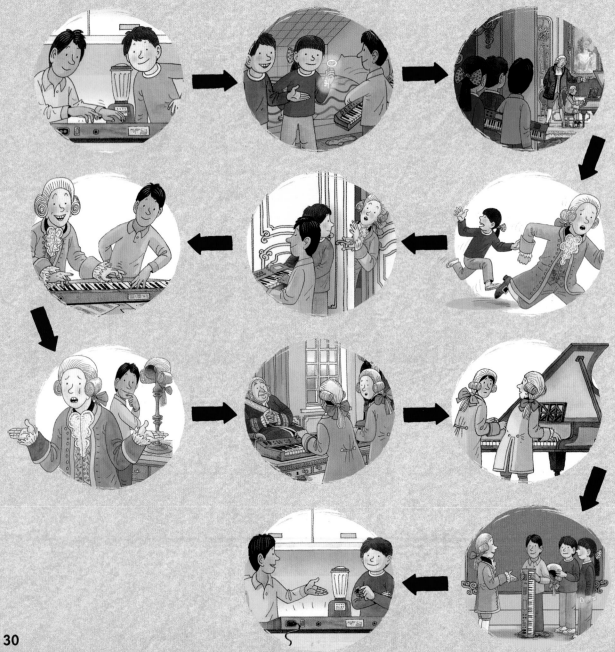

Look Back, Explorers

How did Nadim describe a minuet?

How did Nadim get Wolfgang to open the door?

The children were *whisked* into an adventure. What other words can you think of that mean the same as *whisked*?

Why might Mum think that Nadim is joking when he says that he played with Mozart?

If you had gone on the magic key adventure, what questions would you have asked Wolfgang?

Did you find out who wrote this piece of music?

Explorer Challenge: Mozart (page 19)

What's Next, Explorers?

Now you have read about Nadim performing with Wolfgang, find out all about Mozart as a musician and two other geniuses ...

Explorer Challenge
for *Meet a Genius*

Find out which genius had a badly behaved dog ...